St. Louis Splendor
An Adult Coloring Book

ISBN: 9781681060590

Printed in the United States of America
16 17 18 19 20   5 4 3 2 1

St. Louis Splendor
An Adult Coloring Book

By Jo Ann Kargus

REEDY PRESS

1. Gateway Arch
2. Eads Bridge
3. Old Courthouse
4. Old Cathedral with Gateway Arch
5. Busch Stadium
6. Union Station
7. Bevo Mill
8. Laclede's Landing
9. Anheuser-Busch Brewery
10. World Chess Hall of Fame
11. Soulard Market
12. Cherokee Street
13. Joe's Cafe
14. City Museum (outside)
15. City Museum (inside)
16. Fox Theatre (inside)
17. Grand Center
18. Crown Candy Kitchen
19. The Hill—St. Ambrose with statue
20. Missouri History Museum Library and Research Center
21. New Cathedral
22. The Loop (Pageant, Moonrise, and Tivoli)
23. Ted Drewes
24. Zoo (entrance with animals)
25. Zoo (train by 1904 birdhouse)
26. Muny Pavilion with lake
27. Jewel Box
28. Forest Park Boathouse
29. St. Louis Art Museum (statue)
30. St. Louis Science Center
31. Turtle Park
32. World's Fair Pavilion
33. Tower Grove Park pavilion
34. St. Francis Xavier College Church
35. Missouri Botanical Garden (Climatron)
36. Missouri Botanical Garden (Japanese Garden)
37. Carondelet Park (pavilion, lake)
38. Grant's Farm (Grant's Cabin)
39. Kirkwood Train Station
40. Laumeier Sculpture Park
41. Museum of Transportation
42. Faust Park Carousel
43. Butterfly House at Faust Park
44. Magic House
45. Six Flags
46. Old Chain of Rocks Bridge
47. St. Charles 1st Capitol collage
48. World Bird Sanctuary
49. Old signs of St. Louis
50. St. Louis flag, fleur-de-lis

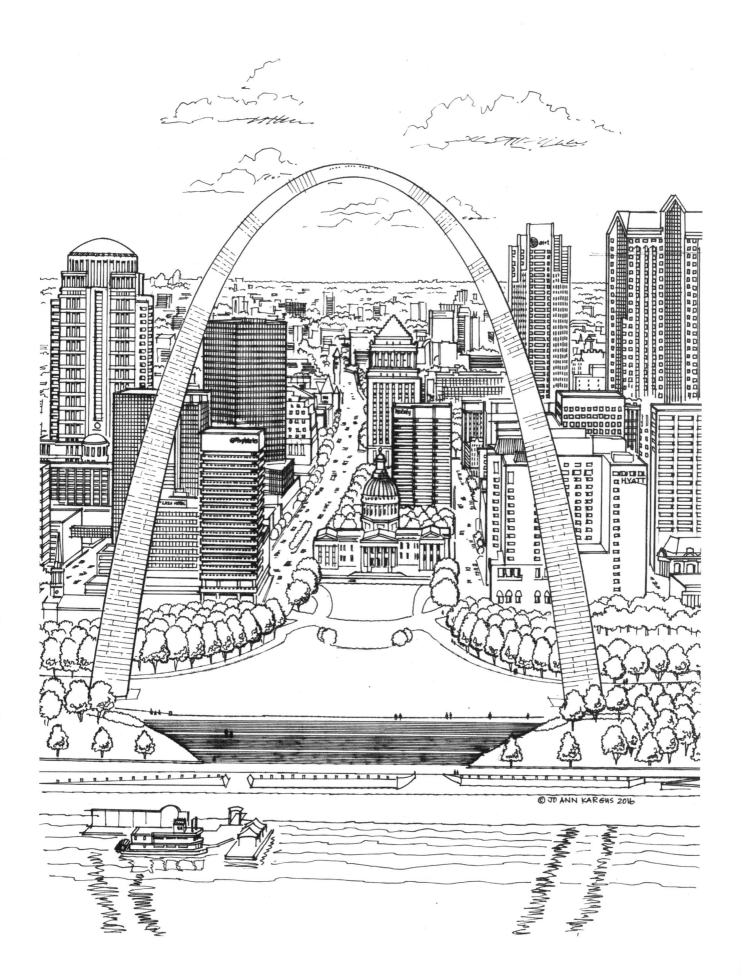

© JO ANN KARGUS 2016

JoANN KARGUS
2016

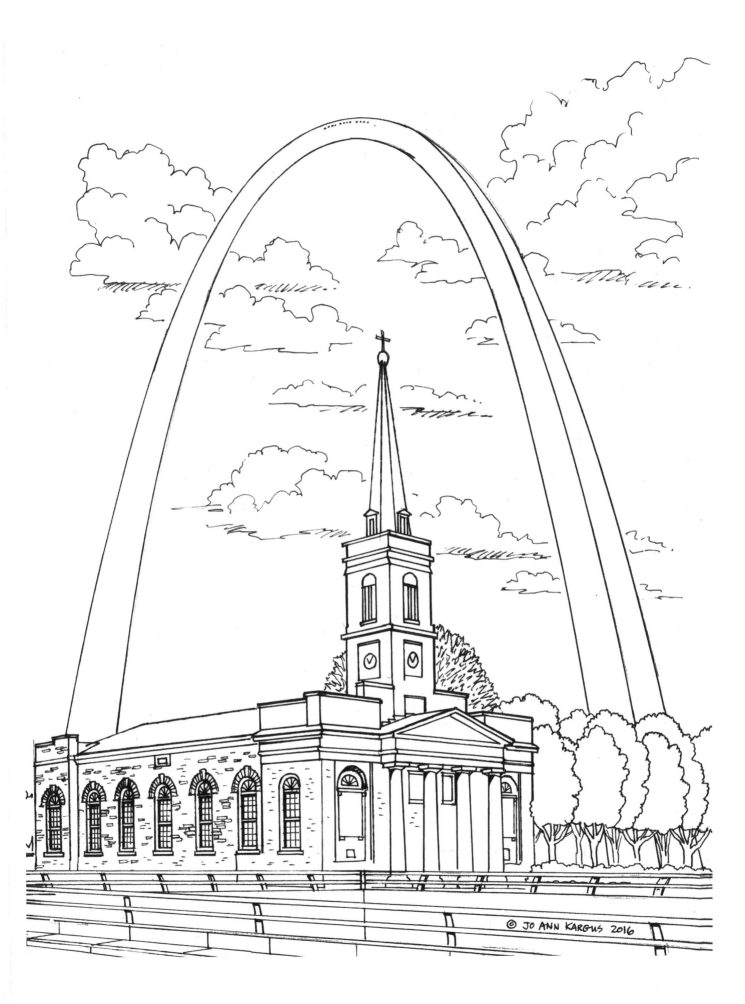

© JO ANN KARGUS 2016

© JO ANN KARGUS
2016

© JOANN KARGUS 2016

© 2016
JOANN KARGUS

CINDERELLA

Cinderella

ENTRANCE

© JOANN KARGUS 2016

© 2016 JO ANN KARGUS

FOX

POWELL

FOX THEATRE

SHELDON · MEMORIAL

GRAND CENTER
ARTS · LIFE

© 2016
JOANN KARGUS

CROWN CANDY

Coca Cola

CROWN CANDY

CROWN CANDY

LUNCH

© JoANN KARGUS 2016

THE ITALIAN IMMIGRANTS

© Jo Ann Kargus 2016

© JOANN KARGUS
2016

© JO ANN KARGUS 2016

© JoAnn Kargus 2016

© JoAnn Kargus
2016

© Jo Ann Kargus 2016

SAINT LOUIS

© JO ANN KARGUS

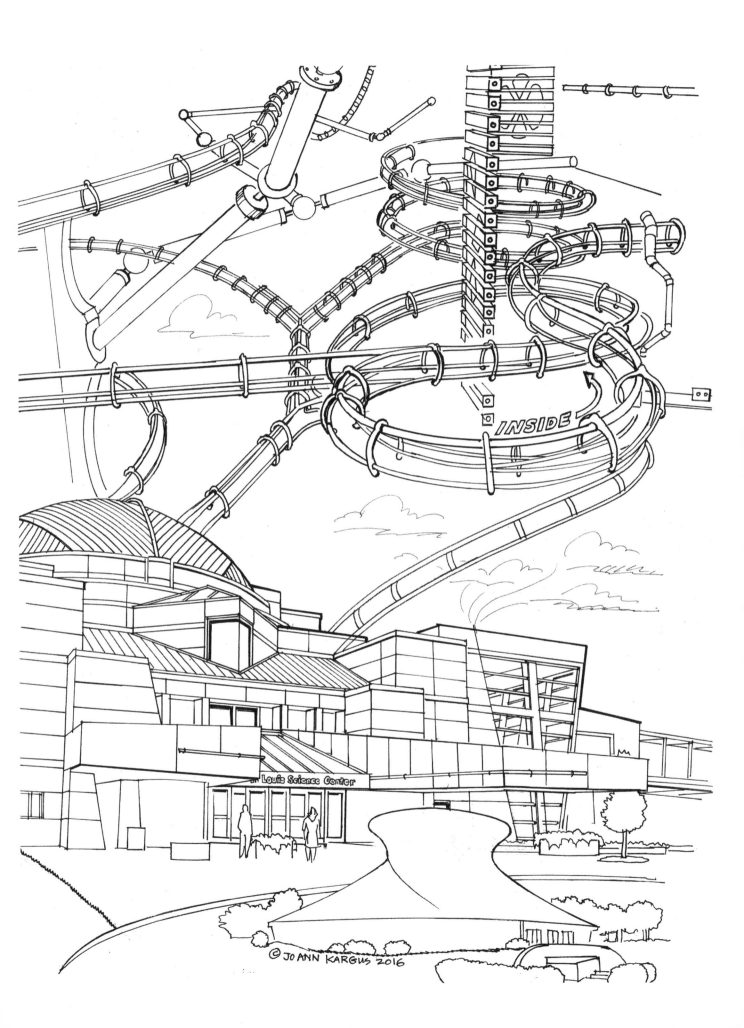

INSIDE

Louis Science Center

© JO ANN KARGUS 2016

2016 © JoAnn Kargus

©JOANN KARGUS
2016

©JO ANN KARGUS 2016

© JO ANN KARGUS 2016

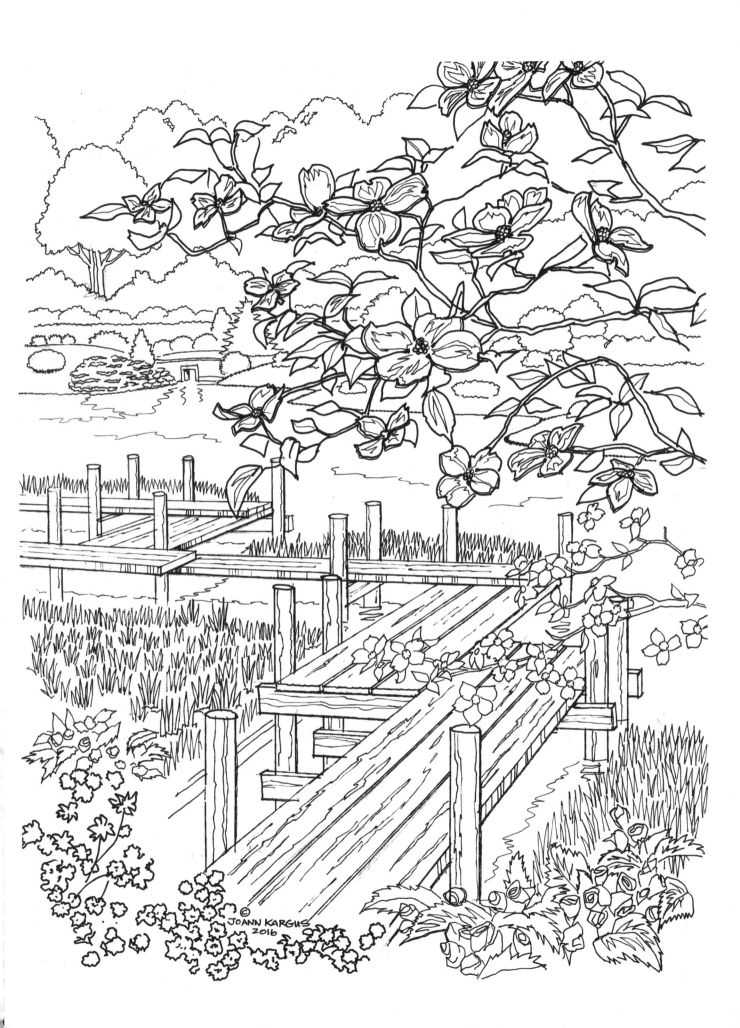

© JO ANN KARGHS 2016

© JO ANN KARGUS 2016

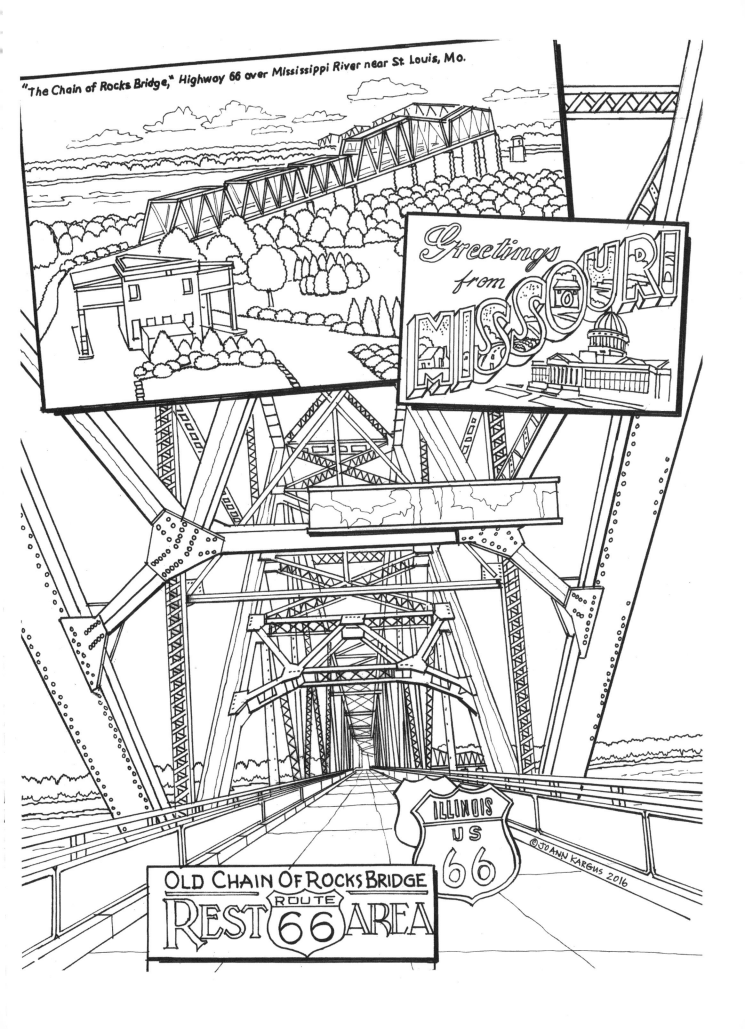

"The Chain of Rocks Bridge," Highway 66 over Mississippi River near St. Louis, Mo.

Greetings from MISSOURI

ILLINOIS US 66

©JoAnn Kargus 2016

OLD CHAIN OF ROCKS BRIDGE
REST ROUTE 66 AREA